201j

Jeffery, Graham

201j

AUTHOR

The Barnabus Bible

TITLE

DATE DUE	BORROWER'S NAME

DATE DUE

201j

GAYLORD

PRINTED IN U.S.A.

D1058721

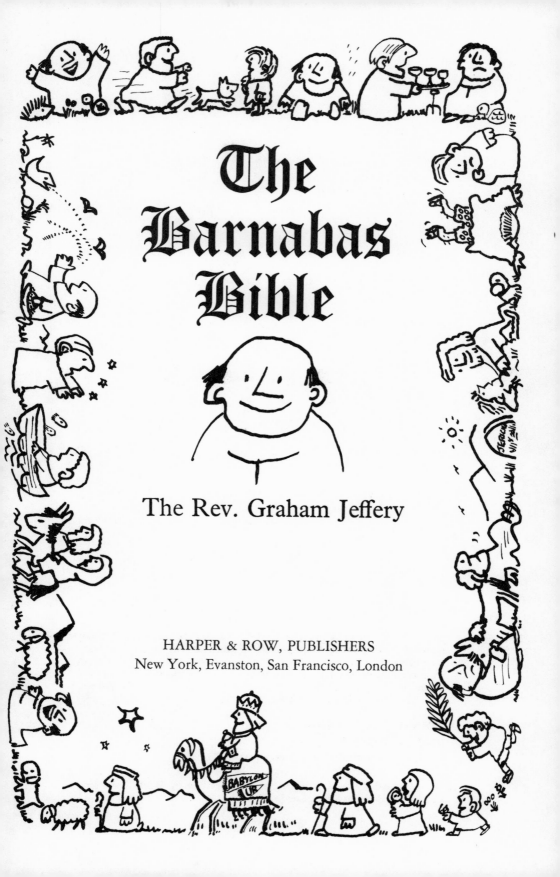

The Barnabas Bible

The Rev. Graham Jeffery

HARPER & ROW, PUBLISHERS
New York, Evanston, San Francisco, London

FIRST UNITED STATES EDITION

ISBN: 0-06-064128-2

LIBRARY OF CONGRESS CATALOG CARD NUMBER: 73-6318

THE BARNABAS BIBLE is published in Great Britain by Wolfe Publishing Limited, 10 Earlham Street, London WC2H 9LP.

The
Barnabas
Bible

THE BIBLE is a strange book. Beginning as it does with one dream, it ends up 2,000 pages later with another. But perhaps this is not so strange, since mankind in general does the same. Dreaming as we do of times when we were young, and the world was better, or looking forward to the future when (we hope) all will be well. Even so, it is surprising to find ourselves, after 2,000 or so pages and 4,000 or so years, back exactly where we started.

In a sense, too, things are more frustrating for

the reader even than that.
For, after reading 2,000
or so pages, we find we
haven't reached the end at all.
John's "new heaven and new
earth" seems as far away as
ever. And the life of Jesus is
still going on, in you and me.

Still, one has to begin
somewhere. So this book,
like the Bible itself, to which
it bears perhaps so little
resemblance, begins . . .

IN THE
BEGINNING

SSSH! THEY'RE
DISCUSSING THE
CREATION.

IT'S A BOARD MEETING
OF CHIEF ANGELS, AND
THEY'RE ARRANGING THE
SOUTH POLE, THE EQUATOR,
THE MEDITERRANEAN
AND THE KOALA BEAR

FLOWERS, GIRAFFES,
THE NORTH SEA, STARS,
PLANETS, WHALES AND
THE HIPPOPOTAMUS.

LIONS, TIGERS, ICE, SNOW
...WHY! WOULD YOU BELIEVE
IT!... THIS IS ONE
       FOR THE BOOKS.

THEY CAN'T GET
ZONING PERMISSION
FOR MOUNT EVEREST.

I LOVE YOU
VERY MUCH, EVE...

THERE'S NO ONE ELSE
QUITE LIKE YOU IN ALL
THE WORLD...

IN FACT...

WOULD YOU BELIEVE IT...

THERE IS NO ONE
ELSE IN **ALL**
THE WORLD!

IT'S LOVELY HERE, EVE. JUST THE TWO OF US.

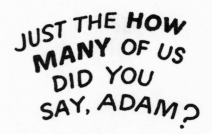

JUST THE **HOW MANY** OF US DID YOU SAY, ADAM?

SORRY, LORD. JUST THE **THREE** OF US, I MEANT TO SAY

I NEVER WAS VERY GOOD AT MATHEMATICS

IT'S NOT MY FAULT
THINGS WENT WRONG,
LORD. I BLAME IT
ALL ON EVE.

DON'T LISTEN TO
HIM, LORD, THE
DEVIL TEMPTED
ME TO DO IT.

AND YOU CAN
HARDLY BLAME
IT ON ME, LORD.

AFTER ALL,
MODERN THEOLOGY
HAS SHOWN THAT
I DON'T EVEN
EXIST.

IT'S VERY DIFFICULT TO
GET PEOPLE TO ACCEPT
RESPONSIBILITY
THESE DAYS.

IS THAT SUPPOSED
TO BE A GIRAFFE?

IT DOESN'T LOOK
MUCH LIKE A
GIRAFFE

I'D ALWAYS RATHER
FANCIED A GIRAFFE AS
SLIM, SLENDER, IMMEASURABLY
TALL: AND FAST AS A
GAZELLE UPON THE
MOUNTAIN TOP

ABLE TO EAT OFF
TREES WITHOUT
STANDING ON
TIP-TOE

HE ISN'T EXACTLY SLIM,
SLENDER, AND FAST AS
A GAZELLE UPON THE
MOUNTAIN TOP

HE ISN'T EVEN
TALL

NEVER MIND, WE'LL CALL
HIM A DONKEY. AFTER ALL
NOBODY ELSE WILL KNOW

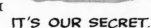

IT'S OUR SECRET.

HOW NICE OF YOU
TO THINK OF
ME

THERE WERE SO
MANY OTHERS YOU
COULD HAVE ASKED

BUT NO! YOU
CREATED ME

WHAT'S THAT?

YOU'VE GOT A
LOT OF WORK
FOR ME TO DO!

LOVING THE FRIENDLESS
COMFORTING THE
BEREAVED

WORKING AND NOT
SEEKING FOR REST,
GOING ON FOR YEARS
AND NOT LOOKING
FOR ANY REWARD

I THOUGHT
THERE WAS A
SNAG TO IT
SOMEWHERE

I SUGGEST NEXT FLOOD YOU
START WITH SOMEONE
QUICKER.

To Abraham
and
his seed
were the promises
made . . .

BUT THERE'S ONE SNAG TO THIS, LORD

OH **DO** LISTEN, LORD. PLEASE TRY TO UNDERSTAND

WE HAVEN'T GOT A SON, AND SARAH IS TOO OLD. NOW, LORD, DO YOU UNDERSTAND?

O LORD, DO LISTEN, HOW **CAN** MY DESCENDANTS BE NUMEROUS AS THE STARS

AND AS MANY AS THE SAND ON THE SEA-SHORE?

AND AS FOR CALLING ME "**FATHER OF MANY NATIONS**" IT'S PLAIN RIDICULOUS

OH NEVER MIND, LORD

DID YOU SAY A BOY, SARAH?

HELLO, LORD. IT'S THE "FATHER OF MANY NATIONS" SPEAKING

ISN'T IT ABOUT TIME YOU GOT A WIFE, ISAAC?

TELL YOU WHAT. GO TO THE WELL, ASK FOR A GLASS OF WATER. AND WHICHEVER GIRL SAYS, "OF COURSE, AND WHAT ABOUT YOUR CAMELS?" THAT'S THE GIRL FOR YOU.

PLEASE CAN I
HAVE A GLASS
OF WATER?

YES OF COURSE YOU
CAN — AND WHAT
ABOUT YOUR
CAMELS?

I NEVER THOUGHT
I'D MARRY A GIRL
WHO WAS FOND
OF CAMELS

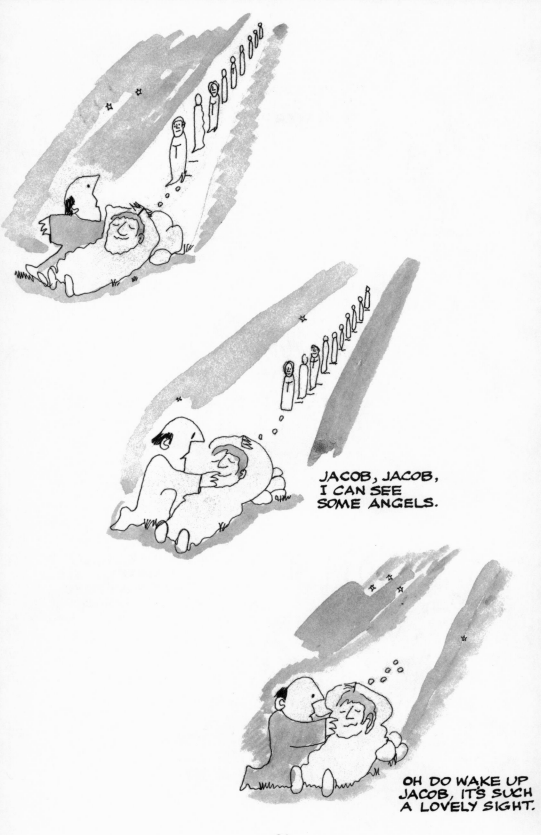

JACOB, JACOB,
I CAN SEE
SOME ANGELS.

OH DO WAKE UP
JACOB, IT'S SUCH
A LOVELY SIGHT.

JACOB, JACOB,
WHAT'S WRONG
WITH YOU.
WAKE UP!

WHAT'S ALL THE
TROUBLE? I
CAN'T SEE ANY
ANGELS.

YOU'RE THE FIRST MAN I
EVER MET WHO COULDN'T
REMEMBER HIS OWN
DREAMS.

HELLO REUBEN, HELLO NAPTHALI.
I HAD A WONDERFUL
DREAM LAST NIGHT

THE STARS AND
THE MOON BOWED
DOWN TO ME

AND YOUR SHEAVES OF
WHEAT FELL DOWN AND
WORSHIPPED MINE

22

AND YOU ALL SAID,
"WHAT A WONDERFUL
BROTHER. AREN'T
WE LUCKY TO HAVE
A BROTHER
LIKE JOSEPH."

I DO BETTER
IN MY DREAMS

JUST BECAUSE YOU'VE GOT
A NEW COAT, JOSEPH, THERE'S
NO NEED TO THINK YOU'RE
BETTER THAN US.

GOD DOESN'T LOOK
ON THE OUTWARD
COAT, YOU KNOW. BUT
ON THE INNER MAN

I QUITE AGREE, BOYS. AND IF
I STRIP AWAY THE OUTER COAT,
WHAT DO YOU SEE?

A MAGNIFICENT
SPECIMEN OF MANHOOD.
THE VERY ENVY OF
HIS DOTING AND
ADORING FAMILY

I THINK ON THE WHOLE
I'D RATHER LOOK ON
THE OUTER COAT

DON'T YOU
BE SO
COCKY,
BOYS

I MAY BE IN A
PIT NOW, AND YOU'
GOT MY COAT

BUT I'M STILL DREAMING OF THE FUTURE: AND EVEN IF I AM SENT AS A SLAVE TO EGYPT

I'LL END UP BETTER OFF THAN YOU, AND THE ENVY OF YOU ALL

Bless This Prison

WELL, I SUPPOSE A PRISON IN EGYPT IS BETTER THAN A HOLE IN ISRAEL.

I SEE A GREAT FUTURE IN FRONT OF YOU, ABDUL.

BACK IN YOUR OLD JOB, SERVING FOR PHARAOH

PHARAOH SAYING "IT'S NICE TO HAVE YOU BACK, ABDUL: HOW DID I EVER DO WITHOUT YOU?"

YOU'LL BE A SUCCESS, ABDUL. BACK IN PHARAOH'S GOOD BOOKS, WITH A STEADY JOB IN THE KITCHEN AHEAD OF YOU

AND OH YES, ONE OTHER THING I FORGOT TO ADD...

YOU'LL FORGET ALL ABOUT ME.

DON'T WORRY, PHARAOH.
I'LL SOON EXPLAIN YOUR
DREAM FOR YOU

THE 7 FAT COWS
ARE 7 GOOD YEARS:
SO YOU'LL HAVE TO
STORE UP ALL
YOUR GRAIN

AND THEN
WE'LL BE ABLE
TO SELL IT
AT A FAT
PROFIT
DURING
THE 7
BAD
YEARS

OF COURSE, IT'S HARD TO ENVISAGE ANYONE WITH SUFFICIENT NERVE, INITIATIVE AND SHEER BRAVADO TO HELP CARRY IT THROUGH

YOU, JOSEPH.

WELL, I'M QUITE OVERCOME, PHARAOH. I REALLY DON'T KNOW WHAT TO SAY. I'M AMAZED AND ASTONISHED

OF COURSE, I'D HAVE BEEN EVEN MORE ASTONISHED IF HE'D CHOSEN SOMEONE ELSE.

OH HOW WONDERFUL!
MY 10 BROTHERS ARE
COMING TO
SEE ME

I'LL GIVE THEM A
GREAT FEAST,
AND SIX SETS.
OF NEW CLOTHING
EACH

ON THE OTHER
HAND, THEY HAVE
BEEN VERY NAUGHTY:
TEARING UP MY
COAT LIKE
THAT.

TELL ME, LORD,
WHAT DO YOU DO
WITH 10
PRODIGAL
BROTHERS?

PERHAPS I SHOULD
JUST GIVE THEM
5 SETS OF NEW
CLOTHING
EACH

BUT I'M TOO YOUNG, LORD:
NOT ESTABLISHED ENOUGH
IN MY PROFESSION. ARE
YOU QUITE SURE YOU'VE
CHOSEN WISELY?

YOU'D DO BETTER
WITH SOMEONE
ELSE MORE SUITED
TO THE JOB

ANYWAY, PHARAOH
WILL NEVER LISTEN
TO ME

HOW CAN I, **ONE** MAN, GET PHARAOH TO RELEASE ALL YOUR PEOPLE FROM EGYPT?

IT'S ABSOLUTELY RIDICULOUS

SOMETIMES I HATE MY OWN CONSCIENCE

PLEASE, PHARAOH,
MAY I GO HOME
NOW?

AREN'T
YOU HAPPY
IN EGYPT
THEN?

ISN'T EGYPT
GOOD ENOUGH
FOR YOU?

I SUPPOSE YOU KNOW WHAT HAPPENS TO LITTLE BOYS WHO WANT TO LEAVE EGYPT BEFORE I SAY!

BUT MY DADDY IS COMING TO COLLECT ME

IN THAT CASE I'D BETTER KEEP RATHER QUIET

DON'T BE PUT OFF BY THE
RED SEA, PHARAOH. I SAW
EXACTLY WHAT MOSES
DID.

IT MAY STAND DEEP AND
IMPENETRABLE TODAY: BUT
ONE WORD FROM ME AND THE
WATERS WILL BE
ROLLED BACK

AND THEN WE'LL BE ABLE
TO PURSUE MOSES ON COMPLETELY
DRY LAND

NEXT TIME I'D BETTER KEEP
A CLOSER WATCH ON MOSES'
RIGHT HAND

THIS IS TO
PUT THE
MILK IN

AND THIS
IS FOR THE
HONEY

BUT
THAT'S STUPID,
BARNABAS

HONEY
DOESN'T
JUST GROW
ON TREES,
YOU KNOW

THE RIVERS AREN'T
LITERALLY FLOWING
WITH MILK AND
HONEY

YOU'VE
GOT
TO
WORK
FOR
IT.

HE'S RIGHT,
REALLY

EVEN SO,
I THINK
I'LL
TAKE
THEM

I NEVER
COULD
DISTINGUISH
BETWEEN
DREAMS
AND
REALITY

I'M NOT NARROW-MINDED. I'LL PRAY TO ANYBODY

YOU SHOULD BE ASHAMED, BARNABAS.

THERE'S ONLY ONE GOD. AND ALL WORSHIP OF ANYTHING ELSE IS SHEER IDOLATRY

AND AS FOR THAT GOLDEN IMAGE OF YOURS, I'M GOING TO SMASH IT TO BITS

THERE!

IT DOESN'T PAY TO BE BROAD-MINDED WHEN MOSES IS AROUND.

WHERE DID YOU GET
THAT TRUMPET?

I JUST CAN'T UNDERSTAND
IT, ELI

THIS TRUMPET SIMPLY
DOESN'T WORK

I'VE WALKED ROUND
GOLIATH'S HOUSE SEVEN
TIMES: AND IT SIMPLY
REFUSES TO FALL
DOWN

BARNABAS, ELI.
HAVE YOU HEARD
THE GOOD
NEWS?

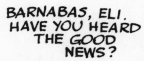

DAVID THE SHEPHERD
BOY HAS SMITTEN GOLIATH
WITH A
SLING AND
FIVE SMOOTH
PEBBLES!

THAT'S ANOTHER THING
ABOUT GOD, ELI.

HE NEVER TRIES THE
SAME TRICK TWICE

WHY DO YOU PRAY TO GOD, DANIEL?

IT'S VERY DANGEROUS, YOU KNOW

THE KING OF BABYLON DOESN'T LIKE IT

AND HE'S GOT **LIONS** AND FIERCE **SOLDIERS** AND **FIERY FURNACES** !

DO YOU MEAN TO TELL ME YOU'RE AFRAID OF A SILLY OLD LION?

IF IT WASN'T FOR MY BOSS THERE WOULDN'T BE ANY LIONS OR TIGERS OR SOLDIERS OR KING OF BABYLON!

THAT'S VERY TRUE

EVEN SO, I HOPE NOBODY SEES US.

46

Yea, I have loved
thee with an
everlasting love . . .

YOU MAY BE RATHER A FAILURE IN SOME WAYS

YOU MAY LACK SUITABLE FRIENDS AND FEEL LONELY AND INADEQUATE

INDEED, YOU MAY BE INADEQUATE

AND I KNOW YOU KEEP MAKING THE SAME MISTAKES AGAIN AND AGAIN

BUT THAT DOESN'T ALTER MY LOVE FOR YOU

AND SO FAR AS I AM CONCERNED, THERE'S NOBODY LIKE YOU IN THE WHOLE WIDE WORLD

THANK YOU, FIDO. I KNOW JUST WHAT YOU ARE THINKING.

REALLY, I WAS HOPING FOR A WALK

NOW THEN, FIDO. I DON'T
WANT YOU CHASING
TIBBY THIS WEEK

AND YOU TOO, TIBBY.
DON'T LET ME CATCH YOU
CHASING THE BIRDS EITHER.

NOT ONE OF THEM GETS
CHASED, REMEMBER, WITHOUT
YOUR HEAVENLY FATHER
NOTICING IT.

AND THAT GOES FOR
YOU AS WELL, BERTHA
AND ANNABEL. NO
PECKING AT LITTLE
INSECTS, NOW. THEY'RE
GOD'S CREATURES, TOO,
YOU KNOW.

IT GETS VERY DULL DURING
BE KIND TO ANIMALS WEEK.

CHEER UP, JOB. THINGS COULD BE WORSE, AFTER ALL

YOU MAY HAVE LOST YOUR FAMILY, AND YOUR SONS AND DAUGHTERS MAY HAVE ALL LEFT YOU

AND I KNOW YOUR HOUSE WAS BURNT DOWN, THE SAME DAY THAT YOU BROKE YOUR ARM AND LEG AND CAUGHT LEPROSY

BUT PERHAPS, JOB, THIS IS ALL A PUNISH-MENT OF SOME KIND FOR THE SORT OF LIFE YOU'VE BEEN LEADING

THERE NOW!
DOESN'T THAT THOUGHT
PUT ALL YOUR TROUBLES
INTO A MORE CHEERFUL
PERSPECTIVE?

AND HELP YOU TO SEE
EVERYTHING AS PART
OF A DIVINE PLAN?

WITH COMFORTERS
LIKE THAT, YOU
DON'T EVEN NEED
AN ILLNESS.

"I WAS JUST GOING TO PRAY TO YOU!"

When I fall,
I shall arise . . .

WHAT'S THE **POINT** OF GETTING UP AGAIN, I SAY!

I ONLY FALL DOWN AGAIN.

ANYWAY, I'VE BEEN FALLING DOWN FOR YEARS

AND **EVERY TIME** I GET UP, IT'S THE SAME OLD STORY

I SIMPLY FALL OVER IN A DIFFERENT PLACE

WHY, HELLO FIDO

I KNOW WHAT YOU WANT. YOU WANT SOMEONE TO THROW THAT STICK FOR YOU.

SOMETIMES I GET UP WITHOUT NOTICING IT.

I DON'T QUITE KNOW
HOW TO PUT THIS...

AND THE LAST THING I
WANT TO DO IS TO
HURT YOU...

BUT I DO, I'M AFRAID,
JUST SOMETIMES...

FIND IT HARD TO BELIEVE
THAT YOU EXIST.

DON'T LET
THAT WORRY YOU,
BARNABAS.

I QUITE AGREE WITH YOU, LORD

IT'S TIME SOMEBODY TOOK A
STAND AND _DID_ SOMETHING

THIS PLOUGHSHARE WON'T BE
MUCH GOOD IF THE PHILISTINES
ATTACK

HOLD IT, LORD,
I WON'T BE
A MOMENT

IT DOESN'T PAY TO
BE TOO MUCH IN ADVANCE
OF YOUR TIME

DON'T YOU BE
SO PROUD OF
YOURSELF,
LOFTY CEDAR OF
LEBANON

YOU MAY TOWER
ABOVE ME NOW,
BUT THE DAY OF
THE LORD WILL
COME

AND THEN THE
PRIDE OF MAN WILL
BE BROUGHT LOW, AND
YOU'LL BE HUMBLED
BEFORE HIM

AND NEXT TIME BE
MORE CAREFUL WHERE
YOU GET SO HUMBLE

CREATION,
PRESERVATION,
REDEMPTION...

FEEDING THE
HUNGRY,
GIVING SIGHT
TO THE
BLIND...

COMFORTING THE BEREAVED,
BLESSING THE LONELY,
MAKING THE LAME TO WALK
AND THE DUMB TO
SPEAK...

FORGIVING SINNERS,
LOVING THOSE WHO
LOVE HIM NOT,
LAYING HIS HANDS
ON LITTLE
CHILDREN...

THESE GOVERNMENT
FORMS ARE THE
ABSOLUTE
LIMIT!

ALWAYS WANTING
TO KNOW YOUR
EMPLOYER'S
OCCUPATION.

New Testament

And the Word
was made flesh
and dwelt among us . . .

WHAT'S THE USE OF IT
UP THERE? I SAY...

IT'S NO EARTHLY
USE AT ALL.

IT NEEDS TO BE DOWN
HERE WHERE WE CAN
USE IT...

NOT STUCK UP THERE,
NO HELP TO ANYONE...

SOMETIMES I PREFER MY DREAMS
TO BE UNATTAINABLE.

And you, child, will be
called the Prophet of
the Highest, for you
shall go before the
Face of the Lord and
prepare His ways

I QUITE AGREE WITH
YOU, ELIZABETH

I CAN'T STAND
THESE
NICKNAMES,
EITHER

JEREMIAH ALWAYS
BEING SHORTENED
TO "JERRY"

MATTHEW
BECOMES "MATT,"
ABRAHAM
BECOMES
"ABE"

AND AS FOR
SAMUEL, THAT
BECOMES "SAM"
IN NO TIME . . .

...JOHN IS ABOUT THE ONLY NAME THEY **CAN'T** TAMPER WITH.

I'M GLAD WE CALLED HIM JOHN.

Hello, JOHN THE BAPTIST

NOW WHERE DID WE GO WRONG?

WHAT DISTRESSES ME MOST
IS THE INCREASING COMMERCIALIZAT
OF CHRISTMAS.

I'M RATHER GOOD
AT JUDGING PICTURES, LORD

THIS ONE, FOR INSTANCE,
IS HARDLY LIKELY TO APPEAL
TO CONTEMPORARY SOCIETY

ITS SUBJECT MATTER IS TOO OBVIOUS
AND EVERYDAY: EVERYBODY'S SEEN A
BABY BEFORE

AND ITS EXECUTION IS TOO
GENTLE AND UNASSUMING BY FAR.
YES, IT IS SIMPLE AND GOOD I
AGREE: BUT IT LACKS THE
AGGRESSIVE SUBTLETY OF
THE MODERN IDIOM.

APART FROM THAT, IT'S IN
A PLAIN WOODEN FRAME: AND
DOUBT IF ANYONE WILL EVEN
NOTICE IT...

I'VE GOT A NASTY FEELING
THAT PICTURE WAS
JUDGING ME

THAT'S WHAT I LIKE
ABOUT YOU, LORD

YOU EXPLAIN
YOURSELF SO WELL
IN JUST A FEW
WORDS

TAKE THIS MESSAGE,
FOR INSTANCE. IT TELL
US EVERYTHING WE
NEED TO KNOW, AND
YET YOU ONLY USE
1 OR 2 WORDS

IN FACT, COME TO LOOK
AT IT, YOU EXPRESS YOURSELF
IN ONLY ONE WORD

THAT'S WHAT I CALL
ECONOMY OF LINE

THAT WAS VERY CONSIDERATE
OF YOU, DEAR

PASSING THE
MARMALADE TO SARAH
WITHOUT BEING
ASKED

YOU'RE GETTING JUST
LIKE YOUR FATHER

NOT YOU, JOSEPH!

HIS HEAVENLY FATHER

SOME PEOPLE
GET ALL THE
CREDIT

I WOULD PLAY WITH YOU,
JOHN, BUT YOUR GAMES
ARE SO SAD.

I LIKE FUNNIER AND HAPPIER
GAMES, YOU KNOW, LIKE
JESUS PLAYS

OF COURSE, JESUS TAKES
HAPPINESS A BIT TOO
FAR: SO I CAN'T
REALLY PLAY WITH
HIM, EITHER

And many shall come
from the East
and from the West
and they shall sit down
with Abraham and Isaac
... in the Kingdom

PLEASE, MUMMY,
CAN THE WHOLE WORLD
COME TO MY
PARTY?

YES, DARLING.
OF COURSE
THEY CAN

MARY AND MARTHA
CAN COME FROM
NEXT DOOR...

MEI LING AND
SHASTRI WILL
REPRESENT OUR
IMMIGRANT
POPULATION...

AND OLD ZACCHEUS THE
TAX COLLECTOR WILL
REPRESENT THE
LONELY AND THE
FORGOTTEN.

IT TAKES GOOD
MANAGEMENT
TO GET THE WHOLE
WORLD IN A ONE-
ROOM
APARTMENT

JESUS WANTS ME TO GO TO HIS PARTY

I'M RATHER SHY ABOUT ACCEPTING INVITATIONS. I DON'T LIKE TO GO UNLESS MY FRIEND MARY IS THERE

BUT THIS DOESN'T SAY IF MARY IS COMING

YES, SHE IS COMING. SO ARE ANDREW AND JAMES AND PETER AND MARTHA

THAT'S GOOD

WHAT ABOUT ABRAHAM AND ISAAC AND RACHEL AND REBECCA AND ELIJAH AND EZEKIEL?

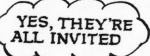

AND EVEN IF YOU HAVE PAID $100
FOR THAT DINNER JACKET
YOU STILL DON'T COMPARE
WITH ME

OH ALL
RIGHT, THEN!
COME ALONG

HE ONLY
WANTED TO
COME TO
JESUS'
PARTY

That I may see...

DON'T YOU WORRY,
JAMES. I KNOW
THE WAY TO
JERICHO

JUST YOU FOLLOW
ME. I KNOW THIS
ROAD LIKE THE BACK
OF MY HAND

THE SECRET OF GETTING
ANYWHERE IN LIFE IS TO GO
WITH SOMEONE WHO'S BEEN
THERE BEFORE, AND
WHO ALSO...

WHOOPS

. . . REMEMBERS THE WAY

OH HOW WONDERFUL!
I'M BEGINNING
TO SEE.

YOU MUST FORGIVE ME, LORD,
BUT I'VE NEVER SEEN
A MAN BEFORE

THAT'S NOT A MAN, BARNABAS.
THAT'S A TREE...

BUT HE'S SO FIRM AND STRONG.
BESIDES, HE'S GOT ALL HIS ARMS
OUT TO WELCOME ME

NO ONE
COULD POSSIBLY
DO ALL
JESUS' WORK
WITH ONLY
TWO ARMS

EVERY TIME I CLOSE
MY EYES, I REMEMBER
WHAT IT WAS LIKE
BEFORE I MET YOU

DO YOU REALIZE, JOSHUA, THIS IS THE FIRST TIME I'VE EVER SEEN MY TOES

YOU SHOULD BE UTTERLY ASHAMED, BARNABAS. THAT'S WHAT I CALL A COMPLETE WASTE OF EYESIGHT

LOOK AT THE WORLD GOD HAS MADE. LIFT UP YOUR EYES TO THE HILLS AND THE STARS AND THE SPACIOUS FIRMAMENT ON HIGH

LOOK AT THE VALLEYS SO RICH WITH CORN, THE RUNNING WATER AND THE BIRDS OF THE AIR

LOOK AT THE LILIES OF THE FIELD, AND THE CHILDREN PLAYING IN THE MARKET PLACE...

SO FAR I'VE COUNTED UP TO SIX

SOME PEOPLE JUST DON'T DESERVE A MIRACLE

7, 8, 9

NO, NO, BOYS, I KEEP TELLING YOU I'M __NOT__ THE MESSIAH.

YOU'VE GOT IT ALL WRONG, DON'T YOU SEE. IT'S __NOT__ ME YOU'VE GOT TO FOLLOW, BUT **HIM**.

IT'S NOT ME YOU SHOULD BE LOOKING AT, AT ALL.

AND NO, I'M
NOT ELIJAH
EITHER: AND
I'M NOT THE
HOPE OF THE
WORLD. AND
I'M NOT THE
SAVIOUR
EITHER.

IT'S NOT EVERYONE
WHO'S KNOWN BY
THEIR NEGATIVES.

THAT'S NOT THE
POINT, BARNABAS

YOU CAN'T JUST
BE A DISCIPLE BECAUSE
YOU LIKE WINE

IT'S <u>YOU</u> WHO'VE GOT TO BE CHANGED,
BARNABAS: NOT THE WATER. THAT'S
THE WHOLE POINT OF THE MIRACLE,
DON'T YOU SEE

YOU'VE TO BE CHANGED FROM
WEAKNESS TO STRENGTH.
FROM SINFULNESS TO HOLINESS,
FROM GLORY INTO GLORY

BUT THAT'S WHY I
WANTED TO JOIN,
MATTHEW

IF YOU GAVE ME WINE
I _WOULD_ BE CHANGED.

COME ON, THOMAS,
YOU'D LOVE TO PLAY

IT'S CALLED "FOLLOW
THE LEADER": LOOK, I'LL
SHOW YOU.

I HAVE TO DO WHAT
ANDREW DOES...

AND ANDREW FOLLOWS JAMES...

AND JAMES DOES WHAT MATTHEW DOES, AND MATTHEW FOLLOWS JESUS...

BUT MATTHEW'S BEEN FOLLOWING ME, BARNABAS. I'VE BEEN UNABLE TO SHAKE HIM OFF ALL AFTERNOON

IN THAT CASE WE'D BETTER GO ON PLAYING "CIRCLES"

BUT BARNABAS,
YOU'VE GOT TO
RENOUNCE
EVERYTHING

IT'S NOT THAT WE
WANT TO BE EXCLUSIVE
OR NARROW-MINDED

BUT YOU'RE
SLOWING THE
REST OF US
DOWN ON OUR
JOURNEY
TO
JERUSALEM

MAY I COME IF I LEAVE
BEHIND MY FISHING ROD?

ROUND THE BAZAAR
TWICE, AND TURN LEFT
AT THE SYNAGOGUE

PAST THE WELL IN
CAPERNAUM SQUARE. BACK
AGAIN TO THE INN

NOW THROUGH
THE LILIES OF
THE FIELD AND
DOWN PAST THE
LOBSTER POTS...

...TO THE
BEACH ITSELF
AND ANDREW'S
BOAT

AND THEN
THEY <u>STOP</u>
ALTOGETHER
AT THE WATER'S
EDGE

IT'S VERY DIFFICULT TO
FOLLOW IN JESUS' FOOTSTEPS
WHEN HE KEEPS GOING
BY BOAT

HERE YOU ARE, DAVID.
HAVE MINE, AND
THEN YOU WON'T
NEED TO BEG

ANYWAY, I'VE GOT
ANOTHER ONE
AT HOME

DON'T WORRY, BARNABAS,
SPRING HAS ARRIVED

WINTER IS OVER
AND PAST AND YOU CAN
HEAR AGAIN THE VOICE
OF THE TURTLE DOVE

THE CLOUDS OF DARKNESS
ARE DISPERSED, AND THE BRIGHT
BEAMS OF GOD'S LOVE...

... ARE WARMING
THE VERY
COCKLES OF
YOUR HEART.

WITH MATTHEW
YOU DON'T NEED AN
UMBRELLA

JUST YOU WAIT,
SAMUEL. YOU MAY
FIND THINGS EASY
NOW.

BUT ONE
DAY THE WIND
WILL BLOW

AND THE RAIN WILL BEAT
DOWN IN TORRENTS, AND
THE THUNDER AND
LIGHTNING WILL
ROAR AND RAGE

AND THEN YOU'LL
WISH YOU'D BUILT
YOUR HOUSE ON FIRM
FOUNDATIONS
LIKE I DID

HOW WAS I TO KNOW WE WERE
IN FOR FINE WEATHER?

DO YOU WANT
TO FACE THE
HATRED OF
THOUSANDS AND
STAND ALONE
FOR ME AMID A
HOSTILE
WORLD?

HOW ABOUT YOUR
JUST
MAKE ME
LOVABLE?

Looking unto Jesus

ISN'T THAT THE
ABSOLUTE
LIMIT!

WHAT A TIME
TO BE ASLEEP,
LORD!

I SIMPLY CAN'T
COPE, JESUS.
THE SITUATION
IS QUITE
OUTSIDE
MY CONTROL

I'M UTTERLY
OVERWHELMED
BY IT ALL, AND
THE ONLY...

POSSIBLE CONSOLATION
I CAN SEE...

IS THAT YOU'RE IN
THE SAME BOAT

PLEASE WAKE UP, JESUS!

YOU SHOULDN'T
BE ASLEEP AT
SUCH A TIME

WE ARE DWARFED
BY CIRCUMSTANCES
OVER WHICH WE
HAVE NO CONTROL

THAT'S IT, LORD
WHAT WAS THAT
YOU SAID?

I SAID, "PEACE, BE STILL".

I'M FEELING
BETTER
ALREADY

IT'S ALL RIGHT, LORD,
I'M COMING

I'M LOOKING STRAIGHT
AT YOU, JESUS

I'VE GOT MY
EYES FIXED
EXACTLY
ON YOU

WELL,
PERHAPS
I HAD
BETTER
REVIEW
THE
SITUATION

TO BE SURE,
I CAN'T REALLY SEE
IT SUPPORTING ME

THE WAVES ARE GETTING HIGHER, AND THAT BOAT'S AN AWFUL LONG WAY OFF

THESE THINGS SEEM TO BE GETTING EVEN BIGGER

AND **BIGGER**

HELP!

SOMETIMES I LOOK AT THE WRONG THING

MARY, DEAR. DO I REMIND YOU AT ALL OF JESUS OF NAZARETH?

NOT REALLY, DARLING.

FOR ONE THING YOU'RE A LITTLE PLUMP. ALSO, YOU'RE A BIT OLDER AND GETTING THIN ON TOP

BESIDES, YOU HAVEN'T GOT A BEARD

SHE NEVER EVEN NOTICED I WAS HELPING WITH THE WASHING-UP.

"DO YOU THINK WHEN I GROW UP
I CAN BE LONELY, DESPISED AND
REJECTED BY ALL MY FRIENDS?"

IT'S MY SON,
**HE'S
COMING
BACK!**

OH HOW WONDERFU
AFTER ALL THESE
YEARS

NO, DON'T SAY
ANYTHING.
YOU'RE
BACK!
THAT'S
ALL
THAT
MATTERS!

IT DOESN'T
MATTER WHAT
YOU'VE DONE...

IT DOESN'T
MATTER HOW
LONG YOU'VE
BEEN AWAY

YOU'RE **HOME**
AGAIN. AND
NOTHING ELSE
MATTERS IN
THE WHOLE
WIDE WORLD!

BUT WILL
MY ELDER
BROTHER
AGREE WITH
YOU?

YOU KNOW MORE
ABOUT THIS
PARABLE THAN
I DO.

IT'S O.K. EVERYBODY.
TOMMY'S BACK

THERE NOW,
THAT'S MY BOY.
HOW ABOUT SOME
SHOES AS WELL?

AND RINGS FOR
HIS FINGER, MABEL.
AND TURN THAT
OVEN ON HIGH

I LAID DOWN
THIS GINGER WINE
FOR YOU THE
YEAR YOU WENT
AWAY. IT'S
JUST RIGHT
FOR YOUR
RETURN,
TOMMY.

NOW EVERYBODY'S
HOME. NOW NOBODY'S
UNHAPPY

ONLY ME AND THE
FATTED CALF...

OH DO JOIN US, SON

IT'S YOUR BROTHER, YOU
KNOW, AND HE'S BEEN
AWAY FOR SUCH A TIME

THEY'RE
ALL ASKING
AFTER
YOU

TOMMY, YOUR MOTHER,
JACK, MARTHA, JOHNNY.
REALLY, THE PARTY
IS NOT
THE
SAME
WITHOUT
YOU

BESIDES, YOUR
MOTHER HAS
MADE ONE
OF YOUR
FAVORITE
PUDDINGS

YOU DON'T
MEAN TREACLE
TART AND
CUSTARD?

IF I DON'T
HURRY UP, THAT
YOUNGER
BROTHER
OF MINE
WILL HAVE
EATEN IT
ALL . . .

HERE'S EDWARD, BOYS.
HE'S COME TO
JOIN US

GOOD OLD
TEDDY

NOT MANY
ELDER BROTHERS
LIKE YOU

I KNEW
HE'D COME
AT LAST

NOW THE
PARTY CAN
BEGIN IN
EARNEST

THIS IS CALLED "STEALING THE
SHOW FROM YOUR
YOUNGER BROTHER"

I LIKE TO
KEEP MY
OPTIONS
OPEN

BUT WE HAVE WORKED
ALL NIGHT, MASTER.

IT'S NOT AS IF
WE HAVEN'T
TRIED

THERE'S SIMPLY
NO POINT IN
GOING ON

IN FACT, I RATHER
DOUBT IF THERE IS
A SINGLE FISH IN
THE WHOLE OF
GALILEE...

SOMETIMES
IT'S NICE TO BE
PROVED WRONG

I DON'T LIKE TO LEAVE YOU THERE, YOU KNOW

THE BIRDS WILL ONLY EAT YOU

THE GROUND DOESN'T LOOK TOO GOOD, EITHER

WHAT WITH THIS SUN AND THE THISTLE IT'S HARD TO SEE YOUR FUTURE CLEARLY

AH WELL, ENOUGH OF DREAMING

THEY CAN'T POSSIBLY GET YOU ALL

THAT'S WHAT I CALL SECURITY IN NUMBERS

THAT LITTLE SEED WILL
NEVER COME TO ANYTHING.
IT'S NOT EVEN WORTH
EATING

IT DOESN'T LOOK
MUCH MORE
PROMISING AS
A PLANT

I'D SOONER PERCH
UP HERE

PERHAPS I HAD
BETTER REVIEW
THE SITUATION

ONE HAS,
AFTER ALL,
TO RECOGNIZE
POLITICAL
REALITIES

AND
YOU
CERTAINLY
DESERVE
FULL
MARKS
FOR
TRYING

I HAVE MADE MY
GREAT DECISION

I NEVER THOUGHT I'D
END UP LIVING IN A
LITTLE
SEED

I'VE DONE IT...

I'VE TURNED THE
WORLD UPSIDE DOWN

THE TREES AND THE BIRDS,
THE FACTORY CHIMNEYS...

THE TEMPLE IS
UPSIDE DOWN, AND SO
ARE THE SHOPS AND
THE ROMAN ARMY...

THE POLITICAL POWER OF HEROD
IS UPSIDE DOWN, PILATE IS ON HIS
HEAD, THE ECONOMIC...

THEY DIDN'T
SEEM
UPSIDE DOWN
TO ME

THAT'S BECAUSE YOU
DON'T SEE THINGS
WITH THE EYE OF
FAITH.

Not a sparrow falls
to the ground
except your Father
notices . . .
Even the hairs of your
head are numbered

SURELY NOT! WELL, TRY
MARTHA E. PHILBY
OF 136
CANNON
HILL
GARDENS

RIGHT AGAIN! NOW TRY
HUGH DEASEY
OF 21
THE CEDARS,
LODGE
AVENUE

HERE'S A HARD ONE.
EMILY JANE ZACHARY
OF 582 CANTELOPE
ROAD

NO? CAUGHT YOU
AT LAST,
HAVE I?

NEVER MIND. NONE OF
US CAN KNOW
__ABSOLUTELY__
EVERYONE

OF COURSE, HE
DOES REALLY.
THERE ISN'T
AN EMILY
JANE
ZACHARY
AT 582
CANTELOPE
ROAD

THE ONLY TROUBLE WITH BUILDING ON YOURSELF

IS THAT ALL THE BRICKS FALL OFF

EVERY TIME YOU GET UP

THAT IS TO SAY...

IF YOU CAN GET UP

SOMETIMES I LOOK AT YESTERDAY

AND SOMETIMES I LOOK AT TOMORROW

BUT WHAT ABOUT ME?

I USED TO BE TOMORROW, YOU KNOW

AND IF YOU WAIT LONG ENOUGH I'LL BE YESTERDAY

THAT'S VERY TRUE

HE ONLY NEEDED A BIT OF PERSUASION

LOOK, MATTHEW,
I'M THE
TALLEST

NO YOU'RE NOT, BARNABAS.
LOOK!

NONSENSE,
MATTHEW. I'M
TALLER THAN
EITHER OF
YOU

HERE'S JESUS. HE'LL TELL YOU I'M
THE TALLEST. HELLO, JESUS,
WHO'S THE TALLEST?

LITTLE GARY IS.
HE'S TALLER THAN
THE LOT OF YOU

THAT'S ONLY BECAUSE
HE'S STANDING
ON YOUR SHOULDERS,
LORD

THAT'S WHAT I CALL
AN UNFAIR
ADVANTAGE

I SEE BARNABAS
OWES ME $2,000

THERE NOW, BARNABAS. I DIDN'T
KNOW YOU FELT LIKE THAT.

LET'S FORGET IT, AND
CALL IT QUITS.

THAT IS MY
FIRST STEP
TOWARDS
FINANCIAL
SOLVENCY

AND MY SECOND
STEP TOWARDS
FINANCIAL
SOLVENCY...

.. IS TO GET
BACK THAT
PENNY
TOMMY OWES
ME ...

WELL I NEVER!
TOMMY'S USING THE
POSTER
I MADE

I'LL SOON PUT
A STOP TO THAT

NOW THEN, TOMMY, HOW ABOUT THAT PENNY?

HELLO, BARNABAS. I FIND YOU OWE ME ANOTHER $2,000

I COULD DO WITH THAT POSTER RIGHT NOW.

96, 97, 98, 99...

WHERE'S BLOSSOM?
HAS ANYONE HERE
SEEN BLOSSOM?

WONDER SHE WASN'T LOST BEFORE

NO HEAD FOR HEIGHTS

COULD BE LOST

ABSOLUTELY

YOU KNOW HOW FORGETFUL SHE IS

WITH ANOTHER FLOCK

NO SHE WASN'T

LOSES HER WAY EASILY

NO, SHE WAS BEHIND **YOU**.

MY DEAR, DID YOU SEE THOSE WOLVES?

WHERE IS SHE?

PERHAPS SHE SLIPPED

LAST SAW HER ON THE DESERT RIDGE

THIS
NEEDS AN
INDEPENDENT
INQUIRY

NEVER MIND, BLOSSOM.
I'M COMING

UP HILLS

DOWN
RECIPICES

UNTIL AT LAST
I FIND YOU

AND THEN **UP** ONTO MY SHOULDERS. **THERE**, BLOSSOM! NOW YOU'RE COMPLETELY SAFE

BUT WHERE ARE WE, SHEPHERD BENJAMIN?

AT LEAST IT'S BETTER TO BE LOST IN COMPANY...

THAT POOR OLD LADY LAST WEEK
WAS ONLY ABLE TO AFFORD
A PENNY

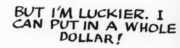

DON'T YOU BE SO SURE OF THAT,
BARNABAS. YOU'VE ONLY PUT
IN A DOLLAR THAT YOU CAN
EASILY
AFFORD

BUT I'M LUCKIER. I
CAN PUT IN A WHOLE
DOLLAR!

...BUT HER PENNY WAS ALL SHE HAD. AND THAT LITTLE PENNY IS WORTH MORE TO GOD THAN ALL THE MONEY IN YOUR WALLET.

OU MEAN TO TELL
ALL THIS IS WORTH
THAN A PENNY?

INFLATION MUST BE EVEN WORSE THAN I REALIZED

FASTER, PEGOTTY,
FASTER.
THERE'S A MAN
IN TROUBLE

HOLD IT, PEGOTTY,
WHILE I POUR
IN THIS OIL
AND WINE

I'LL SOON HAVE HIM
BANDAGED UP.

GOOD GIRL, PEG[C]
WE MUST MAKE
THE INN BEF[O]
NIGHTFALL

...AND IF THERE'S ANYMORE TO PAY,
WE'LL BE BACK THIS WAY IN
TWO WEEKS

THERE NOW, PEGOTTY. DOESN'T
IT GIVE YOU A WARM GLOW TO
FEEL YOU'VE TAKEN PART IN
SUCH AN ADVENTURE?

THE ONLY
GLOW I GOT
WAS WHEN
HE GAVE
ME THAT
CARROT

I WAS ON MY WAY TO
JERICHO WHEN I SAW
HIM THERE

HE WAS COVERED IN BLOOD
IT IS TRUE. BUT AT LEAST
HE WASN'T BEHOLDEN TO
ANYONE. HE WASN'T
DEPENDENT ON ANYBODY

SO I ASK YOU. HOW
COULD I PUT HIM
UNDER AN OBLIGATION
TO ME, AND SAP HIS
INDEPENDENCE BY
DOING HIM GOOD?

I RESPECTED
HIS INTEGRITY.
AND LEFT
HIM FREE.

WHEN ALONG COMES
THIS SOCIAL WORKER
(CONCEITED ASS)

AHA, SAYS HE. A CHAN
TO RELIEVE MY INNE
INADEQUACIES AND
FRUSTRATIONS BY
MAKING SOMEONE
DEPENDENT ON
ME

...I WHO RESPECTED A MAN'S INTEGRITY AND NEVER DENIED HIS INDIVIDUAL RIGHT OF SELF-DETERMINATION

AM **REVILED** IN HOLY WRIT, AND SCORNED BY ALL MANKIND; AND YOU CHRISTIANS CALL **THAT** JUSTICE!

OF COURSE, THERE IS ONE CONSOLATION

AT LEAST I GOT TO JERICHO IN TIME FOR PRAYER MEETING

I'VE GOT A LIST HERE OF MY OWN VIRTUES

JUST LISTEN TO THIS, LORD!

1. I'VE VISITED THE SICK
2. I GAVE $20 TO THE POOR AND
3. I'VE BEEN TO CHURCH EVERY DAY FOR THE PAST TWO MONTHS

THERE NOW! DON'T YOU THINK I'VE DONE RATHER WELL, LORD?

BUT YOU'RE LOOKING AT YOUR OWN VIRTUES, BARNABAS: AND NOT AT ME

SOMETIMES I DO LOOK THE WRONG WAY

WITH SOME PEOPLE
YOU DON'T EVEN NEED
TO TURN THE
OTHER CHEEK

I HOPE TO MAKE A GOOD
IMPRESSION TODAY

AND I CERTAINLY THINK
I'LL STAND OUT AMONG
MY CONTEMPORARIES,
WITH THE EXTRA
HEIGHT THIS WILL
GIVE ME

THERE NOW!
HELLO EVERYBODY...
HOW'D YOU LIKE TO
HEAR RATHER A GOOD
STORY ABOUT A MAN
WHO GOT BEATEN
UP ON THE WAY TO
JERICHO?

THAT'S FUNNY,
I DON'T SEEM TO BE
QUITE THE SUCCESS
THAT I
ANTICIPATED

I HAD HOPED TO TOWER MAJESTICALLY
ABOVE THEM, AND BE LOOKED UP
TO IN ADMIRATION.

IF ANYTHING I'M EVEN
SHORTER THAN NORMAL

THAT'S THE LAST
TIME I TRY STANDING
ON MY DIGNITY.

NOW, NOW, JOHNNY, YOU MUSTN'T TELL SUCH STORIES

100,000 INDEED! YOU'D SCARCELY ENOUGH FOOD FOR YOURSELF

AND DON'T SAY 18,000 OR 10,000 EITHER. THAT'S JUST AS RIDICULOUS

NOW, JOHN, I WANT YOU TO TELL ME THE ABSOLUTE TRUTH

BE ACCURATE, NOW EXACTLY HOW MANY PEOPLE DID YOU SHARE YOUR PICNIC WITH?

ONLY 5,000 DADDY

JUST AS I THOUGHT

YOU BOYS WILL TRY TO MAKE A STORY OUT OF ANYTHING

Behold, we go up
to Jerusalem

YOU'RE MAKING A
PERFECT EXHIBITION
OF YOURSELF, ZACCHEUS

A MAN IN YOUR POSITION
SHOULD ACT HIS AGE: AND
NOT TRY AND APE THE
YOUNGER GENERATION...

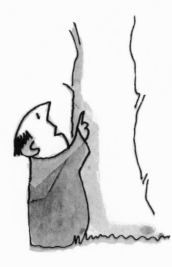

CAN YOU SERIOUSLY
EXPECT US TO RESPECT
YOU ANY MORE? YOU'RE
BRINGING THE WHOLE
ROMAN ADMINISTRATION
INTO DISREPUTE

AND IT'S NO GOOD
YOUR THINKING THE
HEIGHT OF THIS TREE
WILL COMPENSATE
FOR YOUR OWN
PERSONAL INADEQUAC

JESUS WILL
NEVER NOTICE
YOU UP THERE

IT'S PEOPLE LIKE ME WITH OUR FEET SECURELY ON THE GROUND THAT JESUS NOTICES

YES, JESUS, OF COURSE YOU CAN HAVE LUNCH AT MY PLACE. I'LL BE RIGHT DOWN.

HOW IS IT, I WONDER,
THAT CLIMBING ONE
SMALL TREE CAN GAIN
THE ATTENTION OF
THE WORLD?

OH COME ON, PEGOTTY, WE'LL
BE LATE, YOU KNOW WE WILL

THE PROCESSION IS DUE
TO START IN 10 MINUTES
AND WE'RE ALL DEPENDING
ON YOU.

THE CHILDREN ARE READY.
JESUS IS READY. THE PALM
BRANCHES ARE ALL READY
TO BE WAVED.

LOOK PEGOTTY, I'LL GIVE YOU
A NICE JUICY CARROT

OH ALL RIGHT, THEN. WE'LL
ALL GIVE YOU A CARROT IF
YOU PROMISE TO COME

WHO'D EVER HAVE THOUGHT THE
SALVATION OF THE WORLD WOULD
DEPEND ON 12 LITTLE CARROTS?

BUT I PULLED IT OFF TO
SHOUT "HOSANNAH"
WITH, DADDY

AND THE TREE SAID
I COULD. HE LIKES
TO WAVE HIS
ARMS TO
JESUS.

YOU KNOW I CAN'T
SHOUT "HOSANNAH"
UNLESS I WAVE
A BRANCH

ANYWAY, IF I DIDN'T SHOUT HOSANNAH, THE STONES THEMSELVES WOULD START TO SING

ALL RIGHT THEN, NICKY, OFF YOU GO.

I DON'T WANT ALL THE STONES IN THIS GARDEN SHOUTING "HOSANNAH"

I DON'T KNOW WHY, JIMMY:
I JUST FEEL UNHAPPY
THIS EVENING

A SORT OF IMPENDING DOOM,
IF YOU KNOW THE FEELING: RATHER
AS IF LIKE THE FAMILY WAS ALL GOING
TO BREAK UP

IT'S AFFECTED JUDAS TOO,
YOU SEE. HE'S ALL TENSE
AND ON EDGE

AND THE REST OF US AREN'T
MUCH BETTER: I DO WISH WE'D
ASKED MARTHA AND MARY
TO COME

I KNOW IT SOUNDS SILLY
AND SUPERSTITIOUS, BUT
THERE REALLY IS SOME-
THING UNLUCKY...

ABOUT SITTING DOWN
THIRTEEN
AT A TABLE

I'M BEGINNING TO WONDER
WHY THEY EMPLOYED ME.
WE'VE ONLY HAD 13 ALL EVENING,
AND ONE OF THEM LEFT EARLY

AND THIS TALK OF TAKING IT
TO NEW YORK AND THE PROVINCES
IS A PURE PIPE-DREAM.
AT THIS RATE IT WILL HARDLY
RUN TWO DAYS IN JERUSALEM

**I NEEDN'T HAVE WORRIED ABOUT
EARLY RETIREMENT**

TO BE
FRANK,
YOUR CASE
PUZZLES
ME

I CANNOT FOR THE
LIFE OF ME
UNDERSTAND

WHY ON EARTH YOU
INSIST ON
REMAINING
UP THERE

EXTENSIVE ANALYSIS
OF YOUR SUBCONSCIOUS
REVEALS NO HIDDEN
SIN AT ALL

YET YOU
RETAIN A
MARKED
GUILT
COMPLEX

ALMOST ENTIRELY,
IT WOULD SEEM,
ON BEHALF
OF OTHER
PEOPLE

...YOUR FAMILY LIFE
IS QUITE AS
BAFFLING

DESPITE AN EXCELLENT
RELATIONSHIP WITH
YOUR MOTHER

YOU HAVE
DEVELOPED AN
ACUTE FATHER
FIXATION

NEVER HAVING
MARRIED, YOU HAVE
SUBLIMATED
YOUR LOVE

TO INCLUDE
MORE OR
LESS ALL
MANKIND

AND YET YOUR
RELATIONSHIP
WITH THESE
MOST
INADEQUATE
OF
PERSONALITIES...

SEEMS QUITE NORMAL,
NATURAL, AND
UTTERLY BENEFICIAL

HOWEVER, DESPITE
SHOWING FRIENDSHIP
TO THOUSANDS, AND
BEING FOLLOWED—
NOT TO SAY HAUNTED
BY LITTLE CHILDREN
WHEREVER
YOU GO

YOU CONSISTENTLY
EXPERIENCE THE
MOST ACUTE
FEELINGS OF
REJECTION

AND IN CLOSING
YOUR CASE

I HAVE ONLY
THIS TO ADD

GLORY BE
TO THE
FATHER
AND TO THE
SON
AND TO THE
HOLY
SPIRIT.

As it was in the beginning
is now and ever shall be
World without end
Amen

TODAY, I'M
A SUCCESS

IT'S TRUE I CUT OFF
MALCHUS' EAR AND
RAN AWAY WHEN
I GOT
FRIGHTENED

TRUE, I BOASTED I'D STAND
FIRM, AND THEN DENIED
THREE TIMES THAT
I EVEN KNEW
HIM

TRUE, I COULDN'T
KEEP AWAKE AND
WENT TO SLEEP IN
THE GARDEN

BUT DESPITE ALL THIS I'M
A GREAT BIG
BOOMING
SUCCESS!

NOW TO CONVINCE
JUST ONE
PERSON

I AM TO BLAME
FOR I WASHED
MY HANDS
OF HIM

AND I AM
TO BLAME FOR
VOTING
AGAINST
HIM IN
COUNCIL

AND WE SHOUTED
"CRUCIFY HIM!
LET BARABBAS
GO FREE"

AND I
HELPED
WITH HIS
TRIAL
AND
EXECUTION

AND I AM
TO BLAME
FOR RUNNING
AWAY

AT LEAST
I'M NOT TO
BLAME, LOR
I WASN'T
EVEN IN
JERUSALEM

WHAT DO YOU MEAN,
YOU'RE "NOT TO BLAME"!?

DON'T YOU KNOW THAT ALL
THAT IS NECESSARY FOR
THE TRIUMPH OF EVIL...

IS THAT GOOD MEN
SHOULD DO
NOTHING!

SOMETIMES I
FEEL ASHAMED
OF MY OWN
RIGHTEOUSNESS.

And look
I am alive
forever more

QUIET PLEASE, WHILE I
BEGIN MY INVESTIGATIONS

FIRST I MUST EXAMINE
THIS STONE

NOW TO STUDY THE
GRAVE CLOTHES. (YES,
IT'S JUST AS I THOUGHT.)

I HAVE COME TO MY
CONCLUSION, LORD

YOU HAVE DEFINITELY
RISEN FROM
THE DEAD

THE POSITION OF THE
STONE GAVE
IT AWAY.

HOW'D YOU LIKE PEOPLE
TO BELIEVE IN YOU, BECAUSE
OF THE POSITION OF
A STONE?

OH MARY, YOU ARE SILLY. FANCY THINKING JESUS WAS A GARDENER

I'D RECOGNIZE JESUS ANYWHERE LOOK, THERE HE IS!

HELLO, JESUS. IT'S ME, BARNABAS.

DON'T BE SHY JESUS. I KNOW IT'S YOU: I KNEW YOU AS SOON AS I SAW YOU.

SORRY, PAL. I DIDN'T KNOW YOU MEANT ME. I'M GEORGE THE GARDENER

THAT'S CALLED RECOGNIZING JESUS IN THE LEAST OF THOSE HIS BRETHREN

I QUITE AGREE WITH YOU, THOMAS

WE CAN'T BELIEVE UNTIL WE'VE ACTUALLY SEEN HIM

TAKE THIS CHAIR, FOR INSTANCE

I ONLY KNOW IT'S THERE BECAUSE I CAN SEE IT WITH MY EYES. I CAN FEEL IT WITH MY FINGERS.

I CAN TEST ITS PRESENCE BY ACTUALLY SITTING ON IT

THERE!

OF COURSE, NOT ALL VISUAL INSTITUTIONS ARE ACTUALLY INFALLIBLE

197

IT BEATS ME HOW
WE EDITORS ARE
SUPPOSED TO
LIVE

EVER SINCE
THEY KILLED
HIM THERE'S
BEEN SILENCE

NOT A MIRACLE,
NOT A FEEDING,
NOT A HEALING.
NOT EVEN A SIMPLE
CASE OF REPENTANCE

EDITOR HERE. YES,
I'VE GOT IT DOWN.
FLAMES OF FIRE...
HOLY SPIRIT... PETER
PREACHING... CRIPPLE
FROM BIRTH WALKING
ABOUT. YES! YES!
I'LL HAVE A MAN
DOWN RIGHT
AWAY!

I HOPE HE DOESN'T
EXPECT AUTHOR'S
ROYALTIES ON
ALL THIS.

MEN OF ISRAEL,
PLEASE LISTEN

WE'RE NOT DRUNK LIKE YOU
SUPPOSE. WHY! THE BARS AREN'T
EVEN OPEN YET

NO. IT'S GOD'S SPIRIT
MAKES US SO HAPPY

AND HELPS US
BREAK DOWN ALL
BARRIERS OF
SPEECH AND
RACE.
SO THAT
YOU CAN
UNDER-
STAND
US.

WE'RE UNDER THE INFLUENCE OF HIS SPIRIT

IT'S HIS SPIRIT JUST LIKE HE PROMISED YEARS AGO

ANOTHER ADVANTAGE OF THIS FORM OF DRUNKENNESS IS THAT YOU DON'T GET A HANGOVER.

DON'T RUN
AWAY, BOYS

SAUL IS A CHRISTIAN NOW LIKE
THE REST OF US; YOU'VE
NO NEED TO BE AFRAID.

YES, IT'S TRUE. HE WAS
CONVERTED ON THE WAY TO
DAMASCUS, AND HE'S BEEN
A DEVOTED CHRISTIAN
EVER SINCE.

WHY DO YOU WRITE
SUCH AWFULLY LONG
EPISTLES, PAUL ?

WHY NOT TRY
SOMETHING
SHORTER ?

PEOPLE WILL LIKE IT
JUST AS WELL. IN
FACT, WHAT IS
SHORT AND TO
THE POINT IS
OFTEN BETTER
REMEMBERED
THAN WHAT IS
LONG AND
WORDY.

YOU'RE QUITE RIGHT, BARNABAS.
I HADN'T THOUGHT OF
THAT BEFORE.

JUST HOLD ON A MOMENT
WHILE I ADD A PARAGRAPH
OR TWO ABOUT IT TO THE
THESSALONIANS

DEAR ST. PAUL,
THANK YOU FOR YOUR
LAST LETTER...

BUT WE AT CORINTH ENTIRELY
REPUDIATE YOUR SUGGESTION
THAT WE ARE ALL DIVIDED
INTO PETTY FACTIONS.

SOME FOLLOWING YOU,
SOME PETER AND
OTHERS APOLLOS

WE MOST CERTAINLY ARE <u>NOT</u>
DIVIDED, BUT ON THE CONTRARY
STAND UNITED AS ONE FAMILY
OF THE LORD.

WITH LOVE FROM BARNABAS...

THERE. THAT'S FINISHED!

WHAT DO YOU MEAN "WITH LOVE FROM BARNABAS"?!

IT'S ALWAYS "WITH LOVE FROM BARNABAS"

WHY NOT "WITH LOVE FROM STEPHANAS"

CRISPUS! GAIUS!

SO MUCH FOR MY FIRST ECUMENICAL CONFERENCE

207

"LOVE IS KIND, LOVE THINKS NO EVIL"... NOW HOW SHALL I COMPLETE THIS LETTER?

"LOVE IS:"... NOW HOW SHALL I PUT IT? YES, BARNABAS, CAN'T YOU SEE I'M BUSY?

HELLO, PAUL. A STROKE OF LUCK MEETING YOU. MARK AND I WERE ONLY TALKING ABOUT YOU YESTERDAY

208

TELL PAUL ABOUT OUR
JOURNEY, MARK SAID.
AND DON'T FORGET
ABOUT ALL THOSE
MIRACLES I DID.

NOT TO MENTION
MY LATEST
SERMON.
I WONDER
IF YOU'D
LIKE TO
HEAR A
FEW
EXTRACTS?

REALLY, IT
WENT DOWN
WELL
WITH THE
PHILIPPIANS

IN FACT I'M RATHER
THINKING OF HAVING
IT PRINTED...

AND PUT INTO PRIVATE CIRCULATION. AND OH YES...

DO YOU KNOW, BARNABAS... YOU'VE GIVEN ME AN IDEA.

"LOVE SUFFERS LONG, AND IS PATIENT. LOVE BEARS ALL THINGS. LOVE ENDURES ALL THINGS."

THANK YOU, BARNABAS, YOU'RE A GREAT HELP.

IT'S NOT EVERYBODY HELPS PAUL WRITE TO THE CORINTHIANS

HELLO, JESUS. IT'S ONLY ME, JESUS. IT REALLY IS A NICE DAY

I DO HOPE YOU'RE WELL, JESUS. IT'S VERY NICE TO SEE YOU. YES, JESUS. IT'S VERY NICE TO SEE YOU

IT'S NOT EVERYONE WHO'S ON CHRISTIAN-NAME TERMS WITH GOD.

THESE ARE THE WORDS OF THE LORD!

THAT'S WHAT I CALL A FAILURE IN COMMUNICATION.

MY DEEPEST DESIRE, BROTHER,
AND MY MOST EARNEST
SUPPLICATION IN
THE SPIRIT

IS FOR YOUR
SALVATION

AND MY SECOND DEEPEST DESIRE...

IS FOR SOME SUGAR
IN MY TEA.

IT PAYS TO GET YOUR
PRIORITIES RIGHT

I REALLY MUST
HURRY UP

BECAUSE AS SOON AS I
EMPTY ONE BARROW
THERE'S ANOTHER
WAITING

AND THEN
ANOTHER

AND
ANOTHER

WHEW! LORD!
WHAT A WAY TO
BUILD A LIFE!

AT THIS RATE I'LL SOON
HAVE NO THURSDAYS
LEFT

PERHAPS I'D BETTER TAKE
THINGS A BIT SLOWER

THIS IS WHAT THEY
CALL TAKING ONE
DAY AT A
TIME

I DON'T WANT TO KEEP YOU LONG, LORD

SO DO SAY IF YOU'D RATHER GO

AFTER ALL YOU MUST BE NEEDED VERY MUCH IN CHINA AND IRELAND, AFRICA AND' THE MID-EAST

NOT TO MENTION INDIA AND AUSTRALIA, TOPEKA AND BOISE.

DON'T WORRY, BARNABAS

I'M WITH ALL OF THEM ALL THE TIME

AND I CAN SPEND **ALL DAY** WITH YOU IF YOU LIKE

I WAS RATHER HOPING TO CUT MY PRAYERS A BIT SHORT THIS MORNING!

I THINK YOU'RE VERY
UNFAIR, BARNABAS

YOU ALWAYS HIDE,
AND JESUS ALWAYS
HAS TO DO THE
SEEKING

IT'S REALLY YOUR TURN
TO LOOK FOR HIM,
YOU KNOW

BUT I LIKE HIDING,
JIMMY. BESIDES,
JESUS HAS GOT
USED TO
LOOKING
FOR ME

HE KNOWS ALL
MY FAVORITE PLACES:
THE COAL HOUSE,
THE FIG TREE,
BEHIND THE
SYNAGOGUE

JESUS LIKES
LOOKING FOR
ME, NOW

CUCKOO

IN THIS GAME HEARTS ARE
TRUMPS BECAUSE THE
HEART SYMBOLIZES LOVE

AND HEARTS WILL TRUMP
CLUBS OR ANY OTHER
WEAPON OF WAR

AND IT'S NO GOOD YOUR PUTTING
DOWN DIAMONDS BECAUSE
LOVE IS RICHER THAN
DIAMONDS AND MORE
PRECIOUS THAN PEARLS
OR RUBIES

ANOTHER REASON HEAR
ARE TRUMPS IS BECAU
I HAVEN'T GOT ANY
SPADES

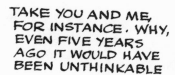
TAKE YOU AND ME, FOR INSTANCE. WHY, EVEN FIVE YEARS AGO IT WOULD HAVE BEEN UNTHINKABLE

I QUITE AGREE WITH YOU, JIMMY. TIMES HAVE DEFINITELY CHANGED

WHO'D HAVE DREAMT WE'D HAVE BEEN SHARING EACH OTHER'S CULTURE, GOING TO THE SAME CHURCH: AND DISCUSSING EACH OTHER'S PROBLEMS IN A FRIENDLY MANNER

YES, JIMMY, THINGS ARE DIFFERENT. AND THE ONLY SNAG I CAN SEE IN THE WHOLE BUSINESS

IS THAT IT TAKES THESE NATURAL DISASTERS TO BRING US TOGETHER

OH DEAR!
I'VE BEEN
TOUCHED
BY A
LEPER

NOW I'VE GOT
LEPROSY: AND
EVERYONE I
TOUCH WILL
GET LEPROSY
TOO

THANK YOU,
JESUS

DID YOU SEE
THAT? JESUS
TOUCHED ME

I WONDER IF
EVERYONE I TOUCH
WILL CATCH
CHRISTIANITY?

I ONLY WANT
TO SAY
"THANK YOU"

NO, REALLY.
I DON'T
WANT
ANYTHING
AT ALL

WELL, YES.
I SUPPOSE
IT <u>DOES</u>
SEEM
STRANGE

I <u>DO</u>
<u>USUALLY</u>
ASK FOR
THINGS,
I AGREE

BUT JUST
FOR TODAY

I WANT TO
SAY THANK YOU,
THANK YOU,
THANK YOU.

SOMETIMES
I LIKE TO
SURPRISE MY
FRIENDS

BUT BARNABAS,
YOU'VE GOT IT
ALL WRONG

JESUS DIDN'T MEAN
YOU JUST TO FORGIVE
70 X 7 = 490 TIMES
AND THEN STOP.

THAT WAS ONLY HIS
WAY OF SAYING YOU'VE
GOT TO GO ON
FORGIVING
ALWAYS

THAT'S ONE MORE FOR IRRITATING ME

LOOK, EVERYBODY. IN PRECISELY TWO MINUTES I'M JUST GOING TO GIVE BARTIMAEUS A PENNY.

COME ON NOW. YOU'RE JUST IN TIME TO SEE IT.

THERE. I THINK EVERYBODY IS HERE

THERE YOU ARE,
BARTIMAEUS.
IT'S NOT ENOUGH
SIMPLY TO DO
GOOD

ONE MUST BE
SEEN TO BE
DOING GOOD.

THE ONLY TROUBLE
WITH SAVING UP
PENNIES

IS THAT WHEN IT'S TIME
TO GO UPSTAIRS AND
SEE JESUS

YOU ALWAYS SEEM
TO KNOCK THEM
OVER.

NOBODY EVER FOUND
A WAY OF CARRYING
A PILE OF
PENNIES

UPSTAIRS

TO

JESUS.

WHAT WITH DEATH DUTIES
AND INFLATION IT'S VERY
HARD TO BE A FINANCIAL
GENIUS THESE DAYS

JUST YOU LISTEN TO THIS, ANDREW.
I'VE COMPOSED A SPECIAL PRAYER
FOR OPENING THIS DOOR.

DEAR LORD, VOUCHSAFE, WE
BESEECH THEE, TO OPEN THIS
HEAVENLY APERTURE SO
THAT WE MAY ENTER INTO
THY PRESENCE

ENABLE US TO ENTER WITH JOY THY CELESTIAL GATES...
AND BE PARTAKERS...

ABSOLUTELY MARVELLOUS

...OF THY MOST HEAVENLY KINGDOM. THERE NOW, ANDREW, WHAT DO YOU THINK OF THAT?

PERHAPS YOU FORGOT TO SAY AMEN

THIS TIME I'LL DEFINITELY
OPEN THAT DOOR

DEAR LORD,
VOUCHSAFE, TO
HEAR ME. I BESEEC
THEE OPEN THOU THE
GATE AND I SHALL
COME IN. UNLOCK THE
DOOR AND I SHALL
ENTER. PULL BACK
THE CURTAIN AND I
SHALL SEE THY
FACE. AMEN.

THAT'S FUNNY.
IT STILL ISN'T
OPEN.

I NEVER MET ANYONE ELSE
WHO BURIED HIS
TALENTS IN THE
GROUND

THEY'LL NEVER
GROW THAT
WAY

YOU'VE GOT TO OPEN
UP YOUR TALENTS AND
SPEND THEM LIKE THIS

MY TALENTS WILL INCREASE AND
MULTIPLY, WHILE YOURS WILL SIMPLY
BE EATEN AWAY BY INFLATION

IN FACT, I CAN'T
THINK OF EVEN
ONE GOOD REASON
WHY YOU BURIED
YOUR TALENTS
AT ALL

ONE GOOD REASON
IS THAT JESUS GAVE
ME A BAG OF
ACORNS

COME ON, PETER. YOU'RE
ALLOWED TO EAT THEM.
JESUS SAYS YOU CAN.

THE GENTILES ARE OUR
BROTHERS NOW, YOU KNOW.
THE CHURCH IS NO LONGER
A PURELY JEWISH
CONCERN

IN FACT THE CHURCH
IS A WORLD-WIDE
FAMILY. THE WORD
"FOREIGN" DOESN'T
APPLY ANY MORE

OH ALL RIGHT, THEN.
BUT ONLY BECAUSE I
LIKE BANANAS

WE'LL HAVE HIM JOINING
THE COMMON MARKET NEXT!

I CAN'T KEEP UP
WITH YOU, PAUL

YOU GO BY CAMEL,
BY FOOT, ON
HORSEBACK,
BY BOAT

YOU'VE BEEN TO CANAAN, ROUND
TURKEY, ALL THROUGH GREECE

IN FACT, ABOUT THE
ONLY PLACE YOU HAVEN'T
BEEN TO IS ROME

THANK YOU, BARNABAS.
YOU'VE GIVEN ME
AN IDEA.

NEXT TIME
I'LL KEEP MY
MOUTH SHUT.

CHEER UP, BARNABAS.
DON'T GIVE UP AND
GROW DISHEARTENED

WE'RE HELPING TO
FOUND A HUGE WORLD-
WIDE SOCIETY

A SOCIETY THAT IN 2,000 YEARS
WILL SPAN THE CONTINENTS AND
UNITE ALL MANKIND IN ONE
HUGE ORGANIZATION

THE ONLY WORLD-
WIDE ORGANIZATION
WE'RE HELPING TO
CREATE IS INTER-
CHURCH TRAVEL.

JUST THINK OF IT, BARNABAS.

IN 2,000 YEARS PEOPLE WILL FOLLOW IN OUR FOOTSTEPS; WALK WHERE WE HAVE WALKED; PRAY WHERE WE HAVE PRAYED

AND WHERE WE STAND ALONE IN THE DESERT, GREAT CATHEDRALS WILL BE FILLED FOR EVENSONG

AND ALL FOR $1,000, ON A 15-DAY PACKAGE TOUR

I'D RATHER HAVE WAITED 2,000 YEARS AND GONE ON THE PACKAGE TOUR

I'M LOOKING BETTER
THAN I WAS
YESTERDAY, PAUL

BUT THAT'S PRIDE,
BARNABAS.

IT'S NO GOOD COMPARING
YOURSELF WITH
YOURSELF. YOU'VE GOT
TO COMPARE YOURSELF
WITH JESUS

AND COMPARED
TO JESUS,
YOU'RE NOT WELL
AT ALL. IN
FACT YOU'RE
RATHER
ILL.

I WONDER IF
PAUL HAS THIS
EFFECT ON
EVERYBODY?

YOU, O LORD, KNOW THE INMOST SECRETS OF OUR HEARTS

YOU KNOW MY PRAYERS EVEN BEFORE THEY ARE UTTERED

YOU KNOW MY DEEPEST NEEDS AND INMOST DESIRES, BETTER THAN I KNOW THEM MYSELF

COME TO THINK OF IT, THERE'S NOT REALLY VERY MUCH I CAN TELL YOU

I MIGHT AS WELL BE GETTING ON WITH THE GARDEN.

REMEMBER NOW, PROMISE YOU'LL COME WITH ME!

You know not
when the Son
of Man will come

 THIS LAST BOOK'S A BIT OF A REVELATION

 "A NEW HEAVEN AND A NEW EARTH"

 HMM! I'VE HEARD THAT DREAM BEFORE

 AND MARK MY WORD, IT NEVER CAME TO ANYTHING

 I CAN'T REALLY SEE IT DOING ANY BETTER THIS TIME

 STILL... I MUSTN'T BE TOO CYNICAL

 ONE GETS USED TO DREAMS IN TIME

 THE ONLY DIFFICULTY I HAVE...

 IS MAKING THEM COME TRUE

YOU'RE ONLY WASTING YOUR FUEL, BARNABAS

IT'S SILLY GOING ROUND
AND ROUND THE BLOCK:
YOU'LL HAVE NO FUEL
LEFT WHEN HE
ARRIVES

AND IT'S NO GOOD ASKING
US FOR SOME. WE'VE
ONLY JUST ENOUGH FUEL
TO MEET HIM AS IT IS

THAT WAY NONE OF US WILL
GET THERE. COME ON, GEORGE

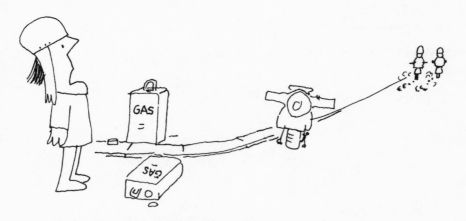

HOW ABOUT **HE WHO HAS TWO GALLONS SHARING WITH HIM THAT HAS NONE!**

IT'S FUNNY HOW ONE'S
FRIENDS GIVE MORE FREE
ADVICE THAN FREE
FUEL

DON'T GO TO
SLEEP, MATTHEW.
HE COULD COME
AT ANY TIME

AT MIDNIGHT.
AT 2 A·M.
AT 5 PAST 3 .
I WOULDN'T LIKE
HIM TO FIND
ME ASLEEP.

I REALLY MUST
KEEP AWAKE .
YOU NEVER KNOW
WHEN HE'LL
ARRIVE

IT'S JUST THESE DARK
UNEXPECTED HOURS WHEN
HE'S LIKELY TO COME .

POOR MATTHEW,
HE'S DROPPED OFF
TO SLEEP. I KNEW
HE WOULD.

WELL, BARNABAS.
DID HE
APPEAR?

I'M SORRY
ABOUT THAT.
BECAUSE HE
CAME TO
ME ALL
RIGHT

SUCH A WONDERFUL
DREAM. A LADDER
GOING TO HEAVEN.
ANGELS GOING UP
AND DOWN. MESSAGES
FROM GOD...THE WORKS!

AND IT'S THAT
SORT OF DREAM
WHICH GIVES A
MAN COURAGE,
AND INSPIRATION,
AND NEW STRENGTH
TO FACE THE DAY
AHEAD!

HAVE YOU EVER NOTICED HOW PEOPLE
WHO'VE HAD VISIONS FORGET TO MAKE
THEIR BEDS?

I'M TRYIN
TO PROVO
HIM TO
ACTION.

I'M WAITING FOR HIM TO COME BACK. THAT'S WHAT I'M DOING

JUST LIKE HE SAID HE WOULD

BUT THAT'S SILLY, BARNABAS

HE WON'T COME BACK FROM UP THERE

YOU'VE GOT TO FIND HIM IN ORDINARY LIFE

IN LOVING YOUR NEIGHBOR, IN DOING GOOD TO THOSE WHO HATE YOU

IN SUFFERING FOR THE TRUTH

DID YOU SAY, "IN SUFFERING FOR THE TRUTH"?

I FIND THIS POSITION MORE COMFORTABLE.

Even so, Lord Jesus —

come quickly . . .